THE ULTIMATE
CINCINNATI REDS
TRIVIA BOOK

A Collection of Amazing Trivia Quizzes
and Fun Facts for Die-Hard Reds Fans!

Ray Walker

Exclusive Free Book

Crazy Sports Stories

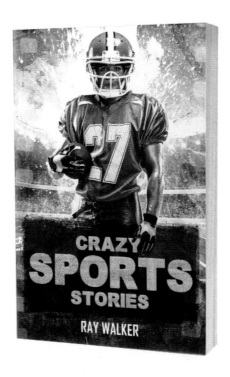

As a thank you for getting a copy of this book I would like to offer you a free copy of my book Crazy Sports Stories which comes packed with interesting stories from your favorite sports such as Football, Hockey, Baseball, Basketball and more.

Grab your free copy over at
RayWalkerMedia.com/Bonus

CONTENTS

INTRODUCTION

The Cincinnati Reds were established in 1881. As one of the oldest teams in MLB, they have consistently proven themselves to be a team that fights hard and is a force to be reckoned with.

They hold five World Series championships, which they won in 1919, 1940, 1975, 1976, and 1990, which was also their most recent World Series appearance. They have won nine National League pennants, three Central Division titles, seven West Division titles, and two wild card berths. They are often a threat in the National League Central Division, having last won it in 2012.

The Cincinnati Reds have retired the uniform numbers of Fred Hutchinson, Pete Rose, Johnny Bench, Joe Morgan, Sparky Anderson, Barry Larkin, Dave Concepción, Ted Kluszewski, Frank Robinson, Tony Pérez, and, of course, Jackie Robinson.

The Reds' current home is the Great American Ball Park, which opened in 2003. They play in one of the most difficult divisions in baseball, the National League Central, alongside the Chicago Cubs, Milwaukee Brewers, Pittsburgh Pirates, and St. Louis Cardinals.

The thing about baseball is that it is a lot like life. There are good times and bad times, good days and bad days, but you have to do your absolute best to never give up. The Cincinnati Reds have proven that they refuse to give up and that they will do anything they need to do to bring a championship to the state of Ohio. Winning is more than possible when you have a storied past like the Cincinnati Reds. They have so much captivating history and so many undeniable player legacies to be profoundly proud of.

With such a storied team past that goes back generations, you're probably already very knowledgeable as the die-hard Reds fan that you are. Let's test that knowledge to see if you truly are the World's Biggest Reds Fan as of the 2020 season, for that's when this book is accurate up till.

CHAPTER 1:

ORIGINS & HISTORY

QUIZ TIME!

1. Which of the following team names did the Reds franchise once go by?

    a. Cincinnati Redlegs
    b. Cincinnati Red Stockings
    c. Cincinnati Red Sox
    d. Both A and B

2. In what year was the Cincinnati Reds franchise established?

    a. 1871
    b. 1881
    c. 1901
    d. 1921

3. The Reds' current home stadium is Great American Ball Park.

    a. True
    b. False

4. Which division do the Cincinnati Reds play in?

    a. American League West
    b. American League Central
    c. National League Central
    d. National League West

5. The Cincinnati Reds have never won a wild card berth.

    a. True
    b. False

6. How many National League pennants has the Cincinnati Reds franchise won?

    a. 6
    b. 7
    c. 8
    d. 9

7. Who is the principal owner of the Cincinnati Reds?

    a. Larry Dolan
    b. Hal Steinbrenner
    c. Bob Castellini
    d. Arturo Moreno

8. Who is the winningest manager in Cincinnati Reds history?

    a. Lou Piniella
    b. Pete Rose
    c. Sparky Anderson
    d. Dusty Baker

9. What is the name of the Cincinnati Reds' Triple-A Team?

a. Nashville Sounds

b. Louisville Bats

c. Omaha Storm Chasers

d. Jacksonville Jumbo Shrimp

10. Who was the first manager of the Reds franchise?

a. O.P. Caylor

b. Buck Ewing

c. Charles Comiskey

d. Pop Snyder

11. The Cincinnati Reds were members of the National League West Division from 1969 to 1993.

a. True

b. False

12. What is the name of the Reds' spring training home stadium?

a. Hohokam Stadium

b. Salt River Fields at Talking Stick

c. Goodyear Ballpark

d. Tempe Diablo Stadium

13. How many appearances has the Cincinnati Reds franchise made in the MLB playoffs?

a. 12

b. 14

c. 16

d. 18

14. How many World Series titles have the Cincinnati Reds won?

    a. 1
    b. 2
    c. 3
    d. 5

15. The Cincinnati Reds' current manager is David Bell.

    a. True
    b. False

16. Which stadium was the first home of the Cincinnati Reds franchise?

    a. Palace of the Fans
    b. Bank Street Grounds
    c. Crosley Field
    d. Riverfront Stadium

17. Who is the current general manager of the Cincinnati Reds?

    a. Mike Rizzo
    b. Dayton Moore
    c. David Forst
    d. Nick Krall

18. How many National League Central Division titles have the Cincinnati Reds won?

    a. 0
    b. 1
    c. 2
    d. 3

19. The Cincinnati Reds won 7 National League West championships during their time in that division.

    a. True
    b. False

20. The Cincinnati Reds franchise was a member of the American Association from 1882 to 1889.

    a. True
    b. False

QUIZ ANSWERS

1. D – Both A and B

2. B – 1881

3. A- True

4. C – National League Central

5. B – False (They won wild card berths in 2013 and 2020.)

6. D – 9

7. C – Bob Castellini

8. C – Sparky Anderson

9. B – Louisville Bats

10. D – Pop Snyder

11. A – True

12. C – Goodyear Ballpark

13. C – 16

14. D – 5

15. A – True

16. B – Bank Street Grounds

17. D – Nick Krall

18. D – 3

19. A – True

20. A – True

DID YOU KNOW?

1. The Cincinnati Reds franchise has had 62 managers so far: Pop Snyder, Will White, O.P. Caylor, Gus Schmelz, Tom Loftus, Charles Comiskey, Buck Ewing, Bob Allen, Bid McPhee, Frank Bancroft, Joe Kelley, Ned Hanlon, John Ganzel, Clark Griffith, Hank O'Day, Joe Tinker, Buck Herzog, Ivey Wingo, Christy Mathewson, Heinie Groh, Pat Moran, Jack Hendricks, Dan Howley, Donie Bush, Bob O' Farrell, Burt Shotton, Chuck Dressen, Bobby Wallace, Bill McKechnie, Hank Gowdy, Johnny Neun, Bucky Walters, Luke Sewell, Earle Brucker Sr., Rogers Hornsby, Buster Mills, Birdie Tebbetts, Jimmy Dykes, Mayo Smith, Fred Hutchinson, Dick Sisler, Don Heffner, Dave Bristol, Sparky Anderson, John McNamara, Russ Nixon, Vern Rapp, Pete Rose, Tommy Helms, Lou Piniella, Tony Pérez, Davey Johnson, Ray Knight, Jack McKeon, Bob Boone, Dave Miley, Jerry Narron, Pete Mackanin, Dusty Baker, Bryan Price, Jim Riggleman, and David Bell.

2. The Cincinnati Reds' current manager is David Bell. He previously managed the minor league Louisville Bats and Carolina Mudcats. He played for 12 seasons for the Cleveland Indians, St. Louis Cardinals, Seattle Mariners, San Francisco Giants, Philadelphia Phillies, and Milwaukee Brewers and he previously coached in the Chicago Cubs and St. Louis Cardinals organizations. As the grandson of Gus Bell, son of Buddy Bell, and brother of Mike Bell, David

9

Bell is a member of one of five families to have three generations play in the MLB. David and Buddy are the fifth father-son duo to serve as MLB managers, joining Connie and Earle Mack, George and Dick Sisler, Bob and Joel Skinner, and Bob and Aaron Boone.

3. Sparky Anderson is the Cincinnati Reds' all-time winningest manager, with a record of 863-586 (.596) W-L%. He also managed the Detroit Tigers. Anderson managed the Reds from 1970 through 1978. He was named the 1984 and 1987 American League Manager of the Year while with Detroit.

4. Bob Castellini is the principal owner of the Cincinnati Reds. He is the chairman of Castellini Co., a fruit and vegetable wholesaler. A lifelong Reds fan, Castellini has been CEO of the team since 2006. In 1989, he became a partner in the Texas Rangers franchise and, in 1993, in the Baltimore Orioles franchise.

5. The Cincinnati Reds have hosted five MLB All-Star Games so far, in 1938 and 1953 at Crosley Field, in 1970 and 1988 at Riverfront Stadium, and in 2015 at Great American Ball Park.

6. Cincinnati Reds pitchers have thrown 16 no-hitters in franchise history. The first was thrown by Bumpus Jones in 1892, and the latest was thrown by Homer Bailey in 2013. The one perfect game in franchise history was thrown on September 16, 1988, by Tom Browning against the Los Angeles Dodgers.

7. The Cincinnati Reds' radio station has been WLW 700 AM, since 1969.

8. The Cincinnati Reds' Double-A farm team is the Chattanooga Lookouts, the High Single-A farm team is the Dayton Dragons, and the Low Single-A farm team is the Daytona Tortugas (or Turtles for those of you who don't speak Spanish).

9. The Reds have four mascots, Mr.Red, Mr.Redlegs, Rosie Red, and Gapper. Gapper is a furry red pet named for a gap in the stadium seats at Great American Ball Park. The three other mascots have baseballs for heads, a la Mr. Met.

10. The Cincinnati Reds have retired 10 numbers so far (11, including Jackie Robinson's No. 42, which is retired league-wide). The latest player to have his number retired was Pete Rose in 2016.

CHAPTER 2:

JERSEYS & NUMBERS

QUIZ TIME!

1. In 1956, the Cincinnati Reds began wearing sleeveless jerseys, worn only once before in the MLB, by the Chicago Cubs.

    a. True

    b. False

2. What are the Cincinnati Reds' official team colors?

    a. Red, white, and blue

    b. Red, black, and white

    c. Navy blue, red, and white

    d. Red, black, and blue

3. During the 1950s, since the color red was connected to communism, blue was introduced into the Cincinnati Redlegs' color scheme.

    a. True

    b. False

4. Which of the following numbers in NOT retired by the Reds?

    a. 1

    b. 5

    c. 13

    d. 15

5. What number does Joey Votto currently wear?

    a. 3

    b. 9

    c. 19

    d. 29

6. What number did Johnny Bench wear during his time with the Reds?

    a. 3

    b. 5

    c. 15

    d. 25

7. Barry Larkin wore the Nos. 15 and 11 during his time with the Cincinnati Reds.

    a. True

    b. False

8. Mariano Duncan, Ben Weber, and which player, are the only three players to have ever worn No. 77 for the Reds?

    a. Pedro Villarreal

    b. Stephen Larkin

    c. Yonder Alonso

    d. Yasiel Puig

9. Who is the only Reds player ever to have worn No. 81?

    a. José De Leon

    b. Eddie Guardado

    c. Josh A. Smith

    d. Rick White

10. No Reds player has ever won No. 0.

    a. True

    b. False

11. What number did Frank Robinson wear as a member of the Cincinnati Redlegs/Reds?

    a. 5

    b. 10

    c. 15

    d. 20

12. What number did Joe Morgan wear as a member of the Cincinnati Reds?

    a. 8

    b. 12

    c. 18

    d. 35

13. Vada Pinson wore No. 28 during his time with the Cincinnati Redlegs/Reds.

    a. True

    b. False

14. What number did Tony Pérez wear as a member of the Cincinnati Reds?

a. 5

b. 27

c. 24

d. 37

15. What number did Dave Concepción wear as a member of the Cincinnati Reds?

    a. 13

    b. 50

    c. 53

    d. Both B and C

16. What number did Brandon Phillips wear as a member of the Cincinnati Reds?

    a. 0

    b. 4

    c. 7

    d. 61

17. During his time with the Cincinnati Reds, what number did George Foster wear?

    a. 10

    b. 14

    c. 15

    d. 19

18. What number does Wade Miley wear?

    a. 20

    b. 22

    c. 36

    d. 38

19. What number did Jim Maloney wear as a member of the Cincinnati Reds?

    a. 23
    b. 26
    c. 43
    d. 46

20. José Rijo wore No. 27 during his time with the Cincinnati Reds.

    a. True
    b. False

QUIZ ANSWERS

1. A - True

2. B – Red, black, and white

3. A – True

4. D – 15

5. C – 19

6. B – 5

7. A – True

8. C – Yonder Alonso

9. B – Eddie Guardado

10. A- True

11. D – 20

12. A – 8

13. A – True

14. C – 24

15. D – Both B and C

16. B – 4

17. C – 15

18. B – 22

19. D – 46

20. A – True

DID YOU KNOW?

1. The Cincinnati Reds have retired 11 uniform numbers overall so far in franchise history: Fred Hutchinson (No. 1), Johnny Bench (No. 5), Joe Morgan (No. 8), Sparky Anderson (No. 10), Barry Larkin (No. 11), Dave Concepción (No. 13), Pete Rose (No. 14), Ted Kluszewski (No. 18), Frank Robinson (No. 20), Tony Pérez (No. 24), and Jackie Robinson (No. 42).

2. Juan Cerros is the only player in Reds history so far to wear No. 71.

3. José De Leon is the only player in Reds franchise history so far to wear No. 87.

4. During his time with the Cincinnati Reds, Homer Bailey wore No. 34.

5. During his time with the Cincinnati Reds, Ken Griffey Sr. wore Nos. 30 and 25.

6. During his time with the Cincinnati Reds, Tom Browning wore Nos. 54 and 32.

7. Jackie Robinson's No. 42 is retired by the Reds as well as the MLB as a whole. No MLB player will ever wear No. 42 again. The Yankees' Mariano Rivera was the last player to wear it.

8. During his time with the Cincinnati Reds, Todd Frazier wore No. 21.

9. During his time with the Cincinnati Reds, Jay Bruce wore No. 32.

10. During his time with the Cincinnati Reds, Johnny Cueto wore No. 47.

CHAPTER 3:

AMERICA'S PASTIME

QUIZ TIME!

1. How many total teams play in Major League Baseball?

    a. 15

    b. 20

    c. 30

    d. 33

2. Major League Baseball was founded in 1903.

    a. True

    b. False

3. Who is the current commissioner of Major League Baseball?

    a. Bart Giamatti

    b. Fay Vincent

    c. Bud Selig

    d. Rob Manfred

4. What year was the National League founded?

    a. 1870

    b. 1876

c. 1903

d. 1911

5. What year was the American League founded?

    a. 1888

    b. 1901

    c. 1903

    d. 1918

6. Major League Baseball is the second wealthiest professional sports league. Which league is the wealthiest?

    a. NBA

    b. NHL

    c. NFL

    d. MLS

7. The Major League Baseball headquarters is located in New York City.

    a. True

    b. False

8. How many games does each Major League Baseball team play per season?

    a. 92

    b. 122

    c. 162

    d. 192

9. In which two U.S. states is Major League Baseball's Spring Training held?

a. California and Florida

b. Arizona and Florida

c. Arizona and California

d. California and Arizona

10. How many stitches does a Major League Baseball baseball have?

a. 98

b. 100

c. 108

d. 110

11. Where is the National Baseball Hall of Fame located?

a. Denver, Colorado

b. Phoenix, Arizona

c. Los Angeles, California

d. Cooperstown, New York

12. All 30 Major League Baseball teams are located in the United States.

a. True

b. False

13. Which current Major League Baseball stadium is the oldest baseball stadium still in use?

a. Angel Stadium

b. Dodger Stadium

c. Fenway Park

d. Wrigley Field

14. Major League Baseball has the highest attendance of any sports league in the world.

    a. True

    b. False

15. Fill in the blank: Seventh Inning _____

    a. Jog

    b. Song

    c. Shake

    d. Stretch

16. William Howard Taft was the first United States president to throw out the ceremonial first pitch at a Major League Baseball game.

    a. True

    b. False

17. It is a Major League Baseball rule that all umpires must wear what color underwear in case they rip their pants?

    a. Tan

    b. Gray

    c. White

    d. Black

18. What year did the first Major League Baseball World Series take place?

    a. 1903

    b. 1905

    c. 1915

    d. 1920

19. Former Major League Baseball Commissioner, Bart Giamatti is the father of actor, Paul Giamatti.

  a. True

  b. False

20. The song traditionally played in the middle of the 7th inning at Major League Baseball games is called *Take Me Out to the Ballpark.*

  a. True

  b. False

QUIZ ANSWERS

1. C – 30

2. A - True

3. D – Rob Manfred

4. B – 1876

5. B – 1901

6. C – NFL

7. A- True

8. C – 162

9. B – Arizona and Florida

10. C – 108

11. D – Cooperstown, New York

12. B – False, 29 out of 30 (The Toronto Blue Jays are located in Canada)

13. C – Fenway Park

14. A – True

15. D – Stretch

16. A – True

17. D – Black

18. A - 1903

19. A – True

20. B – False, *Take Me Out to the Ballgame*

DID YOU KNOW?

1. The average lifespan of a baseball in a Major League Baseball game is 5-7 pitches. This means approximately 5-6 dozen baseballs are used in every Major League Baseball game.

2. The Boston Americans won the very first Major League Baseball World Series. They defeated the Pittsburgh Pirates in 8 games. Today the most games a World Series can go is 7.

3. The New York Yankees currently hold the most World Series titles in Major League Baseball with 27 total.

4. Hot dogs are the most popular food item sold at Major League Baseball ballparks. Over 21 million hot dogs were sold at MLB stadiums in 2014.

5. The longest Major League Baseball game on record occurred on May 9, 1984 between the Chicago White Sox and Milwaukee Brewers. The game lasted 8 hours, 6 minutes. The most innings played in a Major League Baseball game were 26 innings on May 1, 1920. The game was between the Brooklyn Dodgers and Boston Braves.

6. The mound to home plate distance at Major League Baseball ballparks is 60 feet, 6 inches.

7. Before they can be used in a Major League Baseball game, each MLB baseball is rubbed with a special mud to

improve grip and reduce luster. This special mud comes from a specific, secret location in the state of New Jersey.

8. The fastest Major League Baseball game on record took place on September 28, 1919. The game between the New York Giants and Philadelphia Phillies took 51 minutes. An average MLB game is 3 hours.

9. The American League uses a designated hitter. A DH only hits and does not play in the field. In the National League, the pitcher hits instead of using a designated hitter. If an interleague game is being played, whether a DH is used or not is determined by which team is the home team. If the home team is from the American League, each team will use a DH. If the home team is from the National League, each team's pitcher will hit.

10. The distance between each of the four bases in Major League Baseball is 90 feet.

CHAPTER 4:

CATCHY NICKNAMES

QUIZ TIME!

1. What was Frank Robinson's nickname?

    a. The Judge

    b. Pencils

    c. Robbie

    d. Both A and B

2. Joey Votto goes by the nickname "Votto-matic."

    a. True

    b. False

3. What were the Reds nicknamed as a team during the 1970s?

    a. The Dreaded Red

    b. The Big Red Machine

    c. The Cincy Crushers

    d. The Ohio Kings

4. What nickname did Joe Morgan go by?

a. Little Joe

b. The Little General

c. Average Joe

d. Both A and B

5. "Bid" was a nickname. What was Bid McPhee's full name?

a. Alexander Joseph McPhee

b. Joseph Alexander McPhee

c. John Alexander McPhee

d. Alexander John McPhee

6. Which nickname does Tony Pérez go by?

a. Tony the Tiger

b. Big Dog

c. Tough T

d. Both A and B

7. Pete Rose had the nickname "Charlie Hustle."

a. True

b. False

8. "Noodles" was a nickname. What was Noodles Hahn's full name?

a. George Christopher Hahn

b. Christopher George Hahn

c. Frank George Hahn

d. George Franklin Hahn

9. "Bucky" was a nickname. What was Bucky Walters' full name?

a. William Henry Walters

b. Henry William Walters

c. Jackson Henry Walters

d. Jackson William Walters

10. "Sparky" was a nickname. What was former Reds manager Anderson's full name?

a. Lee George Anderson

b. George Lee Anderson

c. Mitch Lee Anderson

d. Harold George Anderson

11. What nickname did Dolf Luque go by?

a. The Cuban Missile

b. Dolfy

c. Lucky

d. The Pride of Havana

12. "Heinie" was a nickname. Heinie Groh's full name was Henry Knight Groh.

a. True

b. False

13. Which nickname does George Foster go by?

a. Scrabble

b. Uno

c. Yahtzee

d. Jumanji

14. What was Tony Mullane's nickname?

a. Count

b. The Apollo of the Box

c. Tony the Tiger

d. Both A and B

15. Red Lucas went by the nickname, "The Nashville Narcissus."

a. True

b. False

16. What nickname does Mike Moustakas go by?

a. Big Mike

b. Moose

c. Taki

d. Double M

17. Paul Derringer went by the nickname "Duke."

a. True

b. False

18. What is Todd Frazier's nickname?

a. Fungo Frazier

b. Flava Fraz

c. The Toddfather

d. Both B and C

19. What nickname does Aroldis Chapman go by?

a. Chappy

b. Rollie

c. Cuban Missile

d. Dis

20. Brandon Phillips goes by the nickname "Dat Dude."

    a. True

    b. False

QUIZ ANSWERS

1. D – Both A and B

2. A- True

3. B – The Big Red Machine

4. D – Both A and B

5. C – John Alexander McPhee

6. B – Big Dog

7. A – True

8. C – Frank George Hahn

9. A – William Henry Walters

10. B – George Lee Anderson

11. D – The Pride of Havana

12. A – True

13. C – Yahtzee

14. D – Both A and B

15. A - True

16. B – Moose

17. A – True

18. D – Both B and C

19. C – Cuban Missile

20. A – True

DID YOU KNOW?

1. "Homer" is a nickname. Homer Bailey's full name is David Dewitt Bailey.

2. Bronson Arroyo had an array of nicknames, including "Saturn Nuts," "Smokey," "Tacks," "Dirty," "BroYo," and "Free Love."

3. Adam Dunn goes by the nickname "Big Donkey."

4. David Ross goes by the nickname "Grandpa Rossy."

5. Johnny Cueto goes by the nicknames "Johnny Beisbol" and "Cinco."

6. Sean Casey goes by the nickname "The Mayor."

7. Ken Griffey Jr. goes by the nicknames "Junior," "The Kid," and "The Natural."

8. Dave Concepción goes by the nickname "El Rey," which means "The King" in Spanish.

9. Trevor Bauer goes by the nickname "Bauer Outage."

10. Anthony DeSclafani goes by the nickname "Disco."

CHAPTER 5:

CHARLIE HUSTLE

QUIZ TIME!

1. What is Pete Rose's full name?

    a. George Peter Rose

    b. Michael Peter Rose

    c. Peter Edward Rose

    d. Peter Howard Rose

2. Rose played his entire 24-season MLB career with the Cincinnati Reds.

    a. True

    b. False

3. Where was Pete Rose born?

    a. Cleveland, Ohio

    b. Cincinnati, Ohio

    c. Columbus, Ohio

    d. Akron, Ohio

4. When was Pete Rose born?

a. April 14, 1941

b. April 14, 1951

c. August 14, 1941

d. August 14, 1951

5. Pete Rose was banned from the MLB after it came to light that he allegedly gambled on baseball games while he played for/managed the Cincinnati Reds.

a. True

b. False

6. How many MLB All-Star Games was Rose named to during his 24-season MLB career?

a. 13

b. 15

c. 17

d. 20

7. Rose was named the National League Rookie of the Year in what year?

a. 1960

b. 1961

c. 1962

d. 1963

8. Pete Rose is a member of the National Baseball Hall of Fame.

a. True

b. False

9. How many National League batting titles did Rose win?

    a. 1
    b. 2
    c. 3
    d. 4

10. What year was he named National League MVP?

    a. 1968
    b. 1970
    c. 1973
    d. 1975

11. How many Silver Slugger Awards did Pete Rose win?

    a. 1
    b. 2
    c. 3
    d. 4

12. Rose was named the 1975 World Series MVP.

    a. True
    b. False

13. How many World Series championships did Rose win?

    a. 2
    b. 3
    c. 4
    d. 5

14. He was inducted into the Cincinnati Reds Hall of Fame and his No. 14 was retired in 2016.

a. True

b. False

15. Pete Rose was the Cincinnati Reds team captain from what year to 1978?

    a. 1965

    b. 1968

    c. 1969

    d. 1970

16. How many home runs did Rose hit in his 24-season MLB career?

    a. 150

    b. 160

    c. 170

    d. 180

17. Rose's career batting average is .303.

    a. True

    b. False

18. How many Gold Glove Awards did he win?

    a. 0

    b. 1

    c. 2

    d. 3

19. How many bases did Rose steal during his MLB career?

    a. 168

    b. 178

c. 188

d. 198

20. Rose had 14,053 plate appearances in his MLB career.

a. True

b. False

QUIZ ANSWERS

1. C – Peter Edward Rose

2. B – False (He also played for the Montreal Expos and Philadelphia Phillies.)

3. B – Cincinnati, Ohio

4. A – April 14, 1941

5. A - True

6. C – 17

7. D – 1963

8. B – False

9. C – 3 (1968, 1969, 1973)

10. C – 1973

11. A – 1 (1981)

12. A – True

13. B – 3

14. A – True

15. D – 1970

16. B – 160

17. A - True

18. C – 2

19. D – 198

20. A – True

DID YOU KNOW?

1. Pete Rose was manager of the Cincinnati Reds from 1984-1989.

2. Pete Rose being inducted into the National Baseball Hall of Fame is still highly debated today. He was not inducted into the Cincinnati Reds Hall of Fame until 2016 due to this conflict.

3. Pete Rose holds 19 MLB records. He also holds 7 National League records.

4. Pete Rose retired with the highest career fielding percentage for a right fielder at 99.14%.

5. Pete Rose's son, Pete Rose Jr., spent 16 years in minor league baseball. In 1997, he played a 11-game stint with the Cincinnati Reds.

6. *Pete Rose: Hits & Mrs.*, was a reality show that followed Pete Rose and his partner Kiana Kim on TLC.

7. Pete Rose was selected as an outfielder on the MLB All-Century Team in 1999.

8. Rose wrote an autobiography entitled *My Prison Without Bars* in 2004.

9. Pete Rose appeared at the WWE's WrestleMania from 1998-2000.

10. Pete Rose became a color analyst on Fox Sports for MLB coverage in 2015.

CHAPTER 6:

STATISTICALLY SPEAKING

QUIZ TIME!

1. Johnny Bench holds the Cincinnati Reds franchise record for the most home runs. How many home runs did he hit during his MLB career?

   a. 369

   b. 379

   c. 389

   d. 399

2. Pitcher Eppa Rixey has the most wins in Cincinnati Reds franchise history with 179.

   a. True

   b. False

3. Which pitcher holds the Cincinnati Reds record for most career shutouts thrown with 32?

   a. Jim Maloney

   b. Bucky Walters

   c. Johnny Vander Meer

   d. Noodles Hahn

4. Which Cincinnati Reds batter holds the single-season record for strikeouts with 205?

    a. Eugenio Suarez

    b. Jay Bruce

    c. Adam Dunn

    d. Drew Stubbs

5. Which pitcher has the most strikeouts in Cincinnati Reds franchise history with 1,592?

    a. Mario Soto

    b. Bronson Arroyo

    c. Jim Maloney

    d. Joe Nuxhall

6. Who has the most stolen bases in Cincinnati Reds franchise history with 568?

    a. Joe Morgan

    b. Bid McPhee

    c. Dave Concepción

    d. Barry Larkin

7. Danny Graves holds the record for most saves in Cincinnati Reds history with 182.

    a. True

    b. False

8. Who holds the Cincinnati Reds record for being intentionally walked with 141?

    a. Frank Robinson

    b. Johnny Bench

c. Joey Votto

d. Pete Rose

9. Which player holds the franchise record for home runs in a season with 52?

   a. Eugenio Suarez

   b. Ted Kluszewski

   c. Johnny Bench

   d. George Foster

10. Which batter holds the single-season Cincinnati Reds record for hits with 230?

   a. Pete Rose

   b. Cy Seymour

   c. Frank McCormick

   d. Vada Pinson

11. Who holds the single-season franchise record for double plays grounded into with 30?

   a. Sean Casey

   b. Ernie Lombardi

   c. Dave Parker

   d. Brandon Phillips

12. Johnny Bench holds the record for the most sacrifice flies in franchise history with 90.

   a. True

   b. False

13. Tony Mullane threw the most wild pitches in franchise history with how many?

a. 164

b. 174

c. 184

d. 194

14. John Reilly holds the Cincinnati Reds single-season record for most triples. How many did he hit in his record 1890 season?

    a. 20

    b. 21

    c. 22

    d. 26

15. Which hitter has the most walks in Cincinnati Reds franchise history with 1,217?

    a. Pete Rose

    b. Joey Votto

    c. Bid McPhee

    d. Barry Larkin

16. Which Cincinnati Reds hitter holds the all-time franchise record for best career batting average at .332?

    a. Bubbles Hargrave

    b. Jake Beckley

    c. Cy Seymour

    d. Edd Rousch

17. Pete Rose holds the Cincinnati Reds record for most runs scored with 1,741.

    a. True

    b. False

18. Pete Rose has the most plate appearances all-time in franchise history with how many?

    a. 9, 344
    b. 10, 344
    c. 11, 344
    d. 12,344

19. Which pitcher holds the Cincinnati Reds record for most saves in a single season with 44?

    a. Jeff Shaw
    b. Jeff Brantley
    c. Danny Graves
    d. Aroldis Chapman

20. Dolf Luque holds the Cincinnati Reds franchise record for most losses with 152.

    a. True
    b. False

QUIZ ANSWERS

1. C – 389

2. A - True

3. B – Bucky Walters

4. D – Drew Stubbs (2011)

5. C – Joe Maloney

6. B – Bid McPhee

7. A – True

8. C – Joey Votto

9. D – George Foster (1977)

10. A – Pete Rose (1973)

11. B – Ernie Lombardi (1938)

12. A – True

13. C – 184

14. D – 26

15. B – Joey Votto

16. C – Cy Seymour

17. A – True

18. D – 12, 344

19. B – Jeff Brantley (1996)

20. A – True

DID YOU KNOW?

1. Eppa Rixey threw the most innings in Cincinnati Reds franchise history with 2,890.2. Coming in second is Dolf Luque, who threw 2,668.2 innings.

2. Cy Seymour had the best single-season batting average in Cincinnati franchise history at .377 in 1905. Coming in second is Bug Holliday, whose batting average was .376 in 1894.

3. Eric Davis holds the Cincinnati Reds franchise record for stolen base percentage with 85.44% success. Bid McPhee holds the Cincinnati Reds franchise record for stolen bases with 568. Pete Rose holds the Cincinnati Reds franchise record for the most times caught stealing at 110 times.

4. Pete Rose has the most extra-base hits in Cincinnati Reds franchise history with 868. Second on the list is Johnny Bench with 794.

5. Adam Dunn holds the Cincinnati Reds franchise record for at-bats per home run at 13.8. This means that, on average, Dunn hit a home run about every 13-14 at-bats.

6. Luis Castillo holds the Cincinnati Reds franchise record for strikeouts per 9 innings pitched at 10.010. This means that, during his time with the Reds, Castillo recorded about 10-11 strikeouts in every 9 innings that he pitched.

7. Shin-Soo Choo holds the single-season Cincinnati Reds record for the most hit by pitches with 26 in 2013. Will

White holds the single-season franchise record for most batters hit with 35 in 1884.

8. Pete Rose holds the Cincinnati Reds franchise record for career doubles hit with 601. Second on the list is Barry Larkin with 441.

9. Will White holds the Cincinnati Reds single-season record for wins with 43 in 1883. Tony Mullane holds the Cincinnati Reds single-season record for most losses with 27 in 1886.

10. Danny Graves holds the Cincinnati Reds franchise record for most saves with 182.

CHAPTER 7:

THE TRADE MARKET

QUIZ TIME!

1. On November 29, 1971, the Cincinnati Reds traded Tommy Helms, Lee May, and Jimmy Stewart to which team for Joe Morgan, Ed Armbrister, Jack Billingham, César Gerónimo, and Denis Menke?

   a. Oakland A's
   b. Houston Astros
   c. San Francisco Giants
   d. Philadelphia Phillies

2. On December 9, 1965. the Cincinnati Reds traded which player to the Baltimore Orioles for Jack Baldschun, Milt Pappas, and Dick Simpson?

   a. Jim Maloney
   b. Tony Pérez
   c. Vada Pinson
   d. Frank Robinson

3. The Cincinnati Reds have made 12 trades with the Arizona Diamondbacks as of the end of the 2020 season.

    a. True

    b. False

4. On May 29, 1971, the Cincinnati Reds traded Frank Duffy and Vern Geishert to which team for George Foster?

    a. Chicago White Sox

    b. New York Mets

    c. San Francisco Giants

    d. Philadelphia Phillies

5. The Cincinnati Reds have made 15 trades with the Colorado Rockies.

    a. True

    b. False

6. On June 15, 1977, the Cincinnati Reds traded Pat Zachry, Doug Flynn, Steve Henderson, and Dan Norman to the New York Mets for which player?

    a. Gary Nolan

    b. Ken Griffey

    c. Dan Driessen

    d. Tom Seaver

7. On March 20, 2006, the Cincinnati Reds traded Wily Mo Pena to which team for Bronson Arroyo?

    a. Seattle Mariners

    b. Boston Red Sox

    c. Pittsburgh Pirates

    d. Washington Nationals

8. On April 7, 2006, the Cincinnati Reds traded Jeff Stevens to the Cleveland Indians for which player?

    a. Adam Dunn

    b. Scott Hatteberg

    c. Brandon Phillips

    d. David Ross

9. On February 10, 2000, the Cincinnati Reds traded Mike Cameron, Antonio Perez, Brett Tomko, and Jake Meyer to the Seattle Mariners for which player?

    a. Sean Casey

    b. Ken Griffey Jr.

    c. Aaron Boone

    d. Barry Larkin

10. The Cincinnati Reds have made only 11 trades with the Florida/Miami Marlins all-time.

    a. True

    b. False

11. On July 26, 2015, the Kansas City Royals traded Brandon Finnegan, Cody Reed, and John Lamb to the Cincinnati Reds for which player?

    a. Aroldis Chapman

    b. Homer Bailey

    c. Pedro Villarreal

    d. Johnny Cueto

12. The Cincinnati Reds have made only 12 trades with the Seattle Mariners.

a. True

b. False

13. How many trades have the Cincinnati Reds made with the San Diego Padres all-time?

    a. 9

    b. 17

    c. 21

    d. 23

14. The Cincinnati Reds have made only 11 trades with the Toronto Blue Jays all-time.

    a. True

    b. False

15. On December 28, 2015, the Cincinnati Reds traded Aroldis Chapman to which team for Eric Jagielo, Caleb Cotham, Rookie Davis, and Tony Renda?

    a. Chicago Cubs

    b. New York Yankees

    c. St. Louis Cardinals

    d. Chicago White Sox

16. On December 8, 1987, the Cincinnati Reds traded Dave Parker to which team for José Rijo and Tim Birtsas?

    a. Pittsburgh Pirates

    b. New York Yankees

    c. California Angels

    d. Oakland A's

17. On December 21, 2018, the Cincinnati Reds traded Homer Bailey, Josiah Gray, and Jeter Downs to the Los Angeles Dodgers for which player, along with Matt Kemp, Alex Wood, James Farmer, and cash considerations.

    a. Freddy Galvis
    b. Trevor Bauer
    c. Yasiel Puig
    d. Eugenio Suarez

18. On December 5, 1957, the Cincinnati Redlegs traded Curt Flood to which team for Marty Kutyna, Willard Schmidt, and Ted Wieand?

    a. Washington Senators
    b. St. Louis Cardinals
    c. Brooklyn Dodgers
    d. Kansas City Athletics

19. On July 20, 1916, which team traded Christy Mathewson, Edd Rousch, and Bill McKechnie to the Cincinnati Reds for Buck Herzog and Red Killefer?

    a. Detroit Tigers
    b. Brooklyn Dodgers
    c. Chicago White Sox
    d. New York Giants

20. The Cincinnati Reds have made 16 trades with the Minnesota Twins/Washington Senators all-time.

    a. True
    b. False

QUIZ ANSWERS

1. B – Houston Astros

2. D – Frank Robinson

3. A – True

4. C – San Francisco Giants

5. A- True

6. D – Tom Seaver

7. B – Boston Red Sox

8. C – Brandon Phillips

9. B – Ken Griffey Jr.

10. A- True

11. D – Johnny Cueto

12. A – True

13. D – 23

14. A – True

15. B – New York Yankees

16. D – Oakland A's

17. C – Yasiel Puig

18. B – St. Louis Cardinals

19. D – New York Giants

20. A- True

DID YOU KNOW?

1. On July 13, 2006, the Cincinnati Reds traded Austin Kearns, Felipe López, and Ryan Wagner to the Washington Nationals for Bill Bray, Royce Clayton, Brendan Harris, Gary Majewski, and Daryl Thompson.

2. On June 15, 2001, the Texas Rangers traded Edwin Encarnación and Ruben Mateo to the Cincinnati Reds for Rob Bell. At the trade deadline in 2009, the Cincinnati Reds traded Edwin Encarnación, Josh Roenicke, and Zach Stewart to the Toronto Blue Jays for Scott Rolen.

3. On December 21, 2007, the Cincinnati Reds traded Josh Hamilton to the Texas Rangers for Danny Herrera and Edinson Volquez.

4. On August 9, 2010, the Cincinnati Reds traded Chris Dickerson to the Milwaukee Brewers for Jim Edmonds.

5. On August 1, 2016, the Cincinnati Reds traded Jay Bruce to the New York Mets for Max Wotell and Dilson Herrera.

6. On December 28, 1957, the Cincinnati Redlegs traded Ted Kluszewski to the Pittsburgh Pirates for Dee Fondy.

7. On October 11, 1968, the Cincinnati Reds traded Vada Pinson to the St. Louis Cardinals for Wayne Granger and Bobby Tolan.

8. The Cincinnati Reds have made only 12 trades with the Seattle Mariners as of the end of the 2020 season.

9. The Cincinnati Reds have made only 11 trades with the Milwaukee Brewers as of the end of the 2020 season.

10. The Cincinnati Reds have made only nine trades with the Tampa Bay Rays as of the end of the 2020 season.

CHAPTER 8:

DRAFT DAY

QUIZ TIME!

1. Johnny Bench was drafted by the Cincinnati Reds in the 2nd round of which MLB draft?

    a. 1965

    b. 1966

    c. 1967

    d. 1968

2. Joey Votto was drafted by the Cincinnati Reds in the 2nd round of which MLB draft?

    a. 2000

    b. 2001

    c. 2002

    d. 2003

3. In the 1st round (3rd overall pick) of the 2011 MLB draft, which team selected Trevor Bauer?

    a. Los Angeles Dodgers

    b. Arizona Diamondbacks

c. Cleveland Indians

d. Cincinnati Reds

4. With which overall pick in the 1st round of the 2007 MLB draft did the Kansas City Royals select Mike Moustakas?

   a. 1st

   b. 2nd

   c. 10th

   d. 12th

5. In the 1st round (18th overall pick) of the 2011 MLB draft, which team selected Sonny Gray?

   a. New York Yankees

   b. Chicago Cubs

   c. Seattle Mariners

   d. Oakland Athletics

6. Brandon Phillips was drafted by which team in the 2nd round of the 1999 MLB draft?

   a. Cleveland Indians

   b. Atlanta Braves

   c. Montreal Expos

   d. Boston Red Sox

7. Barry Larkin was drafted by the Cincinnati Reds in the 2nd round of the 1982 MLB draft but did not sign with them. He was drafted by the Reds again in the 1st round, 4th overall, in 1985.

   a. True

   b. False

8. With which overall pick in the 1st round of the 2007 MLB draft, the Cincinnati Reds selected Todd Frazier.

   a. 4th
   b. 14th
   c. 24th
   d. 34th

9. With which overall pick in the 1st round of the 2005 MLB draft, the Cincinnati Reds selected Jay Bruce.

   a. 2nd
   b. 12th
   c. 22nd
   d. 32nd

10. Zack Cozart was drafted in the 2nd round of the 2007 MLB draft by the Cincinnati Reds.

   a. True
   b. False

11. With which overall pick in the 1st round of the 2004 MLB draft, the Cincinnati Reds selected Homer Bailey.

   a. 2nd
   b. 4th
   c. 7th
   d. 12th

12. Ken Griffey Sr. was drafted by the Cincinnati Reds in the 29th round of the 1969 MLB draft.

   a. True
   b. False

13. With which overall pick in the 1st round of the 1987 MLB draft, the Seattle Mariners selected Ken Griffey Jr.

   a. 1st
   b. 2nd
   c. 3rd
   d. 4th

14. Tom Browning was drafted by the Cincinnati Reds in which round of the 1982 MLB draft.

   a. 4th
   b. 5th
   c. 9th
   d. 10th

15. Sean Casey was drafted by which team in the 2nd round of the 1995 MLB draft?

   a. Detroit Tigers
   b. Cleveland Indians
   c. Pittsburgh Pirates
   d. Boston Red Sox

16. Adam Dunn was drafted by the Cincinnati Reds in the 2nd round of which MLB draft.

   a. 1997
   b. 1998
   c. 1999
   d. 2000

17. Danny Graves was drafted in the 4th round of the 1994 MLB draft by which team?

a. California Angels

b. Florida Marlins

c. New York Mets

d. Cleveland Indians

18. Bronson Arroyo was drafted in the 3rd round of the 1995 MLB draft by which team?

a. Boston Red Sox

b. Arizona Diamondbacks

c. Pittsburgh Pirates

d. Colorado Rockies

19. Scott Rolen was drafted in the 2nd round of the 1993 MLB draft by which team?

a. St. Louis Cardinals

b. Philadelphia Phillies

c. Toronto Blue Jays

d. Cincinnati Reds

20. Mat Latos was drafted by the Cincinnati Reds in the 11th round of the 2006 MLB draft.

a. True

b. False

QUIZ ANSWERS

1. A – 1965
2. C – 2002
3. B – Arizona Diamondbacks
4. B – 2nd
5. D – Oakland Athletics
6. C – Montreal Expos
7. A – True
8. D – 34th
9. B – 12th
10. A – True
11. C – 7th
12. A – True
13. A – 1st
14. C – 9th
15. B – Cleveland Indians
16. B – 1998
17. D – Cleveland Indians
18. C – Pittsburgh Pirates
19. B – Philadelphia Phillies
20. B – False (The San Diego Padres drafted him.)

DID YOU KNOW?

1. Billy Hamilton was drafted in the 2nd round of the 2009 MLB draft by the Cincinnati Reds.

2. Anthony DeSclafani was drafted in the 6th round of the 2011 MLB draft by the Toronto Blue Jays.

3. Edwin Encarnación was drafted in the 9th round of the 2000 MLB draft by the Texas Rangers.

4. David Ross was drafted in the 7th round of the 1998 MLB draft by the Los Angeles Dodgers.

5. Scott Hatteberg was drafted in the 1st round (43rd overall pick) of the 1991 MLB draft by the Boston Red Sox.

6. Jonny Gomes was drafted in the 18th round of the 2001 MLB draft by the Tampa Bay Devil Rays.

7. Jim Edmonds was drafted in the 7th round of the 1988 MLB draft by the California Angels.

8. Reggie Sanders was drafted in the 7th round of the 1987 MLB draft by the Cincinnati Reds.

9. Bret Boone was drafted in the 5th round of the 1990 MLB draft by the Seattle Mariners.

10. Aaron Boone was drafted in the 3rd round of the 1994 MLB draft by the Cincinnati Reds.

CHAPTER 9:

ODDS & ENDS

QUIZ TIME!

1. David Ross was the first MLB contestant on which show?

    a. *Celebrity MasterChef*

    b. *Celebrity Big Brother*

    c. *RuPaul's Celebrity Drag Race*

    d. *Dancing with the Stars*

2. Brandon Phillips' sister Porsha plays in the WNBA for the San Antonio Silver Stars.

    a. True

    b. False

3. Which reality TV show did former Red Jim Edmonds star on with his ex-wife, Meghan?

    a. *Vanderpump Rules*

    b. *90 Day Fiancé*

    c. *The Amazing Race*

    d. *The Real Housewives of Orange County*

4. In 2003, Frank Robinson guest-starred in an episode of which TV show alongside MLB legend Ernie Banks and fellow Red Johnny Bench?

    a. *King of Queens*
    b. *Seinfeld*
    c. *Yes, Dear*
    d. *Everybody Loves Raymond*

5. What does Josh Hamilton have tattooed on his left arm?

    a. A Portrait of Alexander Hamilton
    b. "Hambone"
    c. A Pig
    d. "Hammy"

6. Todd Frazier was a fan of which MLB team when he was growing up?

    a. Cincinnati Reds
    b. Milwaukee Brewers
    c. New York Yankees
    d. New York Mets

7. Joey Votto named his dog, "Maris" after legendary baseball player Roger Maris.

    a. True
    b. False

8. After retiring from baseball, Heinie Groh became a cashier at a what type of establishment?

    a. Convenience store
    b. Racetrack

c. Baseball stadium

d. Fast food restaurant

9. After retiring from baseball, Tony Mullane chose what profession?

a. Real estate agent

b. Car salesman

c. Fireman

d. Police officer

10. Ken Griffey Jr.'s son Trey played in what professional sports league?

a. NBA

b. NHL

c. NFL

d. MLS

11. Which musician's 2015 music video did Ken Griffey Jr. appear in?

a. One Direction

b. Ed Sheeran

c. Drake

d. Macklemore

12. José Rijo was once married to Juan Marichal's daughter, Rosie.

a. True

b. False

13. Adam Dunn appeared in what 2013 movie as a bartender?

a. *Iron Man 3*

b. *Dallas Buyers Club*

c. *Fast and Furious 6*

d. *The Hunger Games: Catching Fire*

14. Todd Frazier won the Little League World Series in 1998.

a. True

b. False

15. What is the name of Bronson Arroyo's 2005 debut album?

a. *Rockin with Bronson*

b. *Life's a Grand Slam*

c. *Covering the Bases*

d. *Another Day, Another Strike Out*

16. Former Red Sean Casey is currently an analyst on MLB Network.

a. True

b. False

17. Which actor played Scott Hatteberg in the movie, *Moneyball*?

a. Chris Pratt

b. Brad Pitt

c. Jonah Hill

d. Ryan Gosling

18. Aaron Boone is the current manager of the what baseball team?

a. Cleveland Indians

b. Miami Marlins

c. New York Yankees

d. Houston Astros

19. Dave Parker owned several of which popular franchises in Cincinnati for 25 years?

a. McDonald's

b. Popeye's Chicken

c. Starbucks

d. Dunkin Donuts

20. Dan Driessen is the uncle of former MLB player Gerald Perry.

a. True

b. False

QUIZ ANSWERS

1. D – *Dancing with the Stars*

2. A – True

3. D – *The Real Housewives of Orange County*

4. C – *Yes, Dear*

5. B – "Hambone"

6. C – New York Yankees

7. A – True

8. B – Racetrack

9. D – Police officer (in the Chicago Police Department)

10. C – NFL

11. D – Macklemore

12. A – True

13. B – *Dallas Buyers Club*

14. A – True

15. C – *Covering the Bases*

16. A – True

17. A – Chris Pratt

18. C – New York Yankees

19. B – Popeye's Chicken

20. A – True

DID YOU KNOW?

1. During the COVID-19 pandemic, former Red Shin-Soo Choo donated $1,000 each to the Texas Rangers' minor leaguers who were unable to play during the stay-at-home order. When he was in the minors, he used to skip meals to be able to buy diapers for his newborn.

2. Noodles Hahn went to veterinary school while playing for the Reds and he became a vet after he retired from baseball.

3. Edd Rousch was the last surviving player from the 1919 World Series. He died in 1988.

4. Bid McPhee, Johnny Bench, and Barry Larkin are the three members of the National Baseball Hall of Fame that played their entire careers with the Cincinnati Reds.

5. When Lonny Frey died at age 99 in 2009, he was the second-oldest living MLB player, the oldest living All-Star, and the last living player that played for all three New York baseball teams in the 1930s and 1940s.

6. Along with many other MLB players, Ken Griffey Jr. was in the famous episode of *The Simpsons* entitled "Homer at the Bat."

7. Wally Berger was the National League's starting center fielder in the very first All-Star Game.

8. "Ted Kluszewski" is in the first line of the chorus to Terry Cashman's song, "Talkin' Baseball."

9. Tom Browning's book, *Tom Browning's Tales from the Reds Dugout*, co-authored by Reds employee Dann Stupp was published in 2006.

10. Ken Griffey Sr.'s father was a teammate of MLB legend Stan Musial in high school.

CHAPTER 10:

OUTFIELDERS

QUIZ TIME!

1. During his 22-season MLB career, Ken Griffey Jr. played for the Seattle Mariners, the Cincinnati Reds, and what other team?

   a. Oakland Athletics
   b. Atlanta Braves
   c. Chicago White Sox
   d. San Diego Padres

2. Dave Parker was named to seven MLB All-Star Games during his 19-season MLB career.

   a. True
   b. False

3. What year was Frank Robinson inducted into the National Baseball Hall of Fame?

   a. 1981
   b. 1982
   c. 1983
   d. 1984

4. Jay Bruce was named the 2008 National League Rookie of the Year.

   a. True
   b. False

5. How many MLB All-Star Games was Adam Dunn named to in his 14-season MLB career?

   a. 1
   b. 2
   c. 4
   d. 6

6. Which of the following teams did former Red George Foster NOT play for during his 18-season MLB career?

   a. New York Mets
   b. Chicago White Sox
   c. San Francisco Giants
   d. St. Louis Cardinals

7. Drew Stubbs played four seasons with the Cincinnati Reds.

   a. True
   b. False

8. How many MLB All-Star Games was Wally Berger named to in his 11-season MLB career?

   a. 1
   b. 2
   c. 3
   d. 4

9. How many World Series championships did Ken Griffey Sr. win in his 19-season MLB career?

   a. 0
   b. 1
   c. 2
   d. 3

10. How many Gold Glove Awards did Eric Davis win during his 17-season MLB career?

   a. 0
   b. 1
   c. 2
   d. 3

11. How many MLB All-Star Games was Vada Pinson named to in his 18-season MLB career?

   a. 1
   b. 2
   c. 3
   d. 4

12. Former Reds Centerfielder Deion Sanders also played in the NFL.

   a. True
   b. False

13. How many times did Edd Roush win the NL batting title during his 18-season MLB career?

   a. 1
   b. 2

c. 3

d. 4

14. Which of the following teams did Gus Bell NOT play in his 15-season MLB career?

    a. Pittsburgh Pirates

    b. Milwaukee Braves

    c. New York Yankees

    d. New York Mets

15. During his 15-season MLB career, César Gerónimo played for the Cincinnati Reds, Houston Astros, and what other team?

    a. Kansas City Royals

    b. Baltimore Orioles

    c. Montreal Expos

    d. California Angels

16. How many seasons did Reggie Sanders spend with the Cincinnati Reds?

    a. 5

    b. 6

    c. 7

    d. 8

17. How many Gold Glove Awards did Jim Edmonds win during his 17-season MLB career?

    a. 4

    b. 6

    c. 8

    d. 10

18. Paul O'Neill spent eight seasons with the Cincinnati Reds and nine seasons with what other MLB team?

    a. Oakland Athletics
    b. New York Yankees
    c. Boston Red Sox
    d. Minnesota Twins

19. How many Gold Glove Awards did César Cedeño win in his 17-season MLB career?

    a. 0
    b. 1
    c. 3
    d. 5

20. Mike McCormick missed the 1944 and 1945 MLB seasons due to military service.

    a. True
    b. False

QUIZ ANSWERS

1. C – Chicago White Sox

2. A – True

3. B – 1982

4. B – False (He finished in 5th place.)

5. B – 2

6. D – St. Louis Cardinals

7. A – True

8. D – 4

9. C – 2

10. D – 3

11. D – 4

12. A – True

13. B – 2 (1917 and 1919)

14. C – New York Yankees

15. A – Kansas City Royals

16. D – 8

17. C – 8

18. B – New York Yankees

19. D – 5

20. A – True

DID YOU KNOW?

1. Ken Griffey Jr. spent 10 of his 21 seasons in MLB with the Cincinnati Reds. He also played for the Seattle Mariners and Chicago White Sox. He is a member of the National Baseball Hall of Fame, MVP, a 13x MLB All-Star, 10x Gold Glove Award winner, 7x Silver Slugger Award winner, All-Star MVP, and Major League Player of the Year.

2. Frank Robinson spent 13 seasons of his 22-season MLB career with the Cincinnati Reds. He also played for the Baltimore Orioles, Cleveland Indians, California Angels, and Los Angeles Dodgers. He is a member of the National Baseball Hall of Fame, 2x MVP, NL Rookie of the Year, Triple Crown winner, a 14x MLB All-Star, Gold Glove Award winner, batting title champion, All-Star MVP, Major League Player of the Year, AL Manager of the Year, 2x World Series champion, and World Series MVP.

3. Dave Parker spent 4 seasons of his 19-season MLB career with the Cincinnati Reds. He also played for the Pittsburgh Pirates, Oakland A's, California Angels, Toronto Blue Jays, and Milwaukee Brewers. He is a 7x MLB All-Star, 3x Gold Glove Award winner, 3x Silver Slugger Award winner, MVP, All-Star MVP, and 2x batting title champion.

4. Jay Bruce spent nine seasons with the Cincinnati Reds. He currently plays for the Philadelphia Phillies. So far in his career, he has also played for the New York Mets,

Cleveland Indians, and Seattle Mariners. As of the end of the 2020 season, he is a 3x MLB All-Star and 2x Silver Slugger Award winner.

5. George Foster spent 11 seasons of his 18-season MLB career with the Cincinnati Reds. He also played for the New York Mets, San Francisco Giants, and Chicago White Sox. He is a 5x MLB All-Star, Silver Slugger Award winner, MVP, All-Star MVP, and 2x World Series champion.

6. Eric Davis spent 9 seasons of his 17-season MLB career with the Cincinnati Reds. He also played for the Los Angeles Dodger, St. Louis Cardinals, Baltimore Orioles, Detroit Tigers, and San Francisco Giants. He is a 2x MLB All-Star, 3x Gold Glove Award winner, 2x Silver Slugger Award winner, and World Series champion.

7. Vada Pinson spent 11 seasons of his 18-season MLB career with the Cincinnati Reds. He also played for the Kansas City Royals, California Angels, Cleveland Indians, and St. Louis Cardinals. He was a 4x MLB All-Star and Gold Glove Award winner.

8. Ken Griffey Sr. spent 12 seasons of his 19-season MLB career with the Cincinnati Reds. He also played for the Seattle Mariners, New York Yankees, and Atlanta Braves. He is a 3x MLB All-Star, All-Star MVP, and 2x World Series champion.

9. Ken Griffey Sr. spent 8 seasons of his 17-season MLB career with the Cincinnati Reds. He also played for the

New York Yankees. He is a 5x MLB All-Star, batting title champion, and 5x World Series champion.

10. Edd Rousch spent 12 seasons of his 18-season career with the Cincinnati Reds. He also played for the New York Giants, Newark Peppers, and Chicago White Sox. He is a member of the National Baseball Hall of Fame, 2x batting title champion, and World Series champion.

CHAPTER 11:

INFIELDERS

QUIZ TIME!

1. What year was Joe Morgan inducted into the National Baseball Hall of Fame?

    a. 1989

    b. 1990

    c. 1991

    d. 1993

2. Barry Larkin was inducted into the National Baseball Hall of Fame in 2012.

    a. True

    b. False

3. How many MLB All-Star Games was Tony Pérez named to during his 23-season MLB career?

    a. 3

    b. 5

    c. 7

    d. 9

4. How many games did Pete Rose play during his 24-season MLB career?

    a. 3,462
    b. 3,562
    c. 3,662
    d. 3,762

5. How many Gold Glove Awards did Brandon Phillips win during his 17-season MLB career?

    a. 1
    b. 2
    c. 3
    d. 4

6. Which year didTodd Frazier win the MLB Home Run Derby?

    a. 2013
    b. 2014
    c. 2015
    d. 2016

7. Dave Concepción spent his entire 19-season MLB career with the Cincinnati Reds.

    a. True
    b. False

8. How many Gold Glove Awards did Scott Rolen win during his 17-season MLB career?

    a. 2
    b. 3

c. 6

d. 8

9. What year did the Cincinnati Reds retire Ted Kluszewski's No. 18?

   a. 1997

   b. 1998

   c. 1999

   d. 2000

10. Joey Votto was named the NL MVP in what year?

    a. 2008

    b. 2009

    c. 2010

    d. 2011

11. How many World Series championships did Lonny Frey win in his 14-season MLB career?

    a. 0

    b. 1

    c. 2

    d. 3

12. Scott Hatteberg played his entire MLB career with the Cincinnati Reds.

    a. True

    b. False

13. How many MLB All-Star Games was Sean Casey named to during his 12-season MLB career?

a. 0

b. 1

c. 2

d. 3

14. How many Silver Slugger Awards did Bret Boone win in his 14-season MLB career?

a. 0

b. 1

c. 2

d. 3

15. How many seasons did Edwin Encarnación spend with the Cincinnati Reds?

a. 5

b. 6

c. 7

d. 8

16. Zack Cozart spent seven seasons with the Cincinnati Reds.

a. True

b. False

17. How many MLB All-Star Games was Aaron Boone named to in his 12-season MLB career?

a. 0

b. 1

c. 2

d. 3

18. Which of the following teams did former Red, Buddy Bell NOT play for in his 18-season MLB career?

    a. Texas Rangers

    b. Cleveland Indians

    c. Houston Astros

    d. Los Angeles Dodgers

19. How many seasons did Dan Driessen spend with the Cincinnati Reds?

    a. 10

    b. 11

    c. 12

    d. 14

20. Ron Oester played his entire 13-season MLB career with the Cincinnati Reds.

    a. True

    b. False

QUIZ ANSWERS

1. B – 1990

2. A- True

3. C – 7

4. B – 3,562

5. D – 4

6. C – 2015

7. A – True

8. D – 8

9. B – 1998

10. C – 2010

11. C – 2

12. B – False (He played for the Reds, Oakland A's, and Boston Red Sox.)

13. D – 3

14. C – 2

15. A – 5

16. A – True

17. B – 1

18. D – Los Angeles Dodgers

19. C – 12

20. A- True

DID YOU KNOW?

1. Joe Morgan spent 8 seasons of his 22-season MLB career with the Cincinnati Reds. He also played for the Houston Astros, Oakland A's, San Francisco Giants, and Philadelphia Phillies. He is a member of the National Baseball Hall of Fame, 2x MVP, a 10x MLB All-Star, 5x Gold Glove Award winner, Silver Slugger Award winner, All-Star MVP, 2x Major League Player of the Year, and 2x World Series champion.

2. Barry Larkin spent his entire 19-season MLB career with the Cincinnati Reds. He is a member of the National Baseball Hall of Fame, MVP, a 12x MLB All-Star, 3x Gold Glove Award winner, 9x Silver Slugger Award winner, and World Series champion.

3. Tony Pérez spent 16 seasons of his 23-season MLB career with the Cincinnati Reds. He also played for the Montreal Expos, Philadelphia Phillies, and Boston Red Sox. He is a member of the National Baseball Hall of Fame, a 7x MLB All-Star, All-Star MVP, and 2x World Series champion.

4. Pete Rose spent 19 seasons of his 24-season MLB career with the Cincinnati Reds. He also played for the Montreal Expos and Philadelphia Phillies. He is a 17x MLB All-Star, 2x Gold Glove Award winner, Silver Slugger Award winner, MVP, NL Rookie of the Year, 3x batting title champion, World Series MVP, and 3x World Series champion.

5. Dave Concepción spent his entire 19-season MLB career with the Cincinnati Reds. He is a 9x MLB All-Star, 5x Gold Glove Award winner, 2x Silver Slugger Award winner, All-Star MVP, and 2x World Series champion.

6. Brandon Phillips spent 11 seasons of his 17-season MLB career with the Cincinnati Reds. He also played for the Cleveland Indians, Los Angeles Angels, Atlanta Braves, and Boston Red Sox. He is a 3x MLB All-Star, 4x Gold Glove Award winner, and Silver Slugger Award winner.

7. Ted Kluszewski spent 11 seasons of his 15-season MLB career with the Cincinnati Reds. He also played for the Pittsburgh Pirates, Chicago White Sox, and Los Angeles Angels. He was a 4x MLB All-Star.

8. Scott Rolen spent 4 seasons of his 17-season MLB career with the Cincinnati Reds. He also played for the Philadelphia Phillies, St. Louis Cardinals, and Toronto Blue Jays. He is a 7x MLB All-Star, 8x Gold Glove Award winner, Silver Slugger Award winner, NL Rookie of the Year, and World Series champion.

9. Dan Driessen spent 12 seasons of his 15-season MLB career with the Cincinnati Reds. He also played for the Montreal Expos, San Francisco Giants, St. Louis Cardinals, and Houston Astros. He is a 2x World Series champion.

10. Joey Votto has spent his entire MLB career with Cincinnati Reds so far. He has been with the Reds since 2007. As of the end of the 2020 season, he is a 6x MLB All-Star, Gold Glove Award winner, and MVP.

CHAPTER 12:

PITCHERS AND CATCHERS

QUIZ TIME!

1. During his 14-season MLB career, José Rijo played for the Cincinnati Reds, New York Yankees, and what other team?

    a. Florida Marlins

    b. Houston Astros

    c. Oakland A's

    d. Seattle Mariners

2. Johnny Bench spent his entire 17-season career with the Cincinnati Reds.

    a. True

    b. False

3. During his 12-season MLB career, Jim Maloney played 11 seasons with the Cincinnati Reds and 1 season with what other MLB team?

    a. New York Yankees

    b. Chicago Cubs

    c. Texas Rangers

    d. California Angels

4. During his 21-season MLB career, Eppa Rixey played 13 seasons with the Cincinnati Reds and 8 seasons with what other MLB team?

    a. Boston Red Sox

    b. Philadelphia Phillies

    c. Detroit Tigers

    d. Philadelphia Athletics

5. What year was Tom Seaver inducted into the National Baseball Hall of Fame?

    a. 2

    b. 3

    c. 4

    d. 5

6. How many MLB All-Star Games was Bucky Walters named to in his 16-season MLB career?

    a. 2

    b. 4

    c. 6

    d. 8

7. David Ross was never named to an MLB All-Star Game.

    a. True

    b. False

8. How many NL ERA titles did Dolf Luque win during his 20-season MLB career?

a. 0

b. 1

c. 2

d. 3

9. How many MLB All-Star Games was Paul Derringer named in his 15-season MLB career?

a. 1

b. 2

c. 4

d. 6

10. How many seasons did Homer Bailey spend with the Cincinnati Reds?

a. 7

b. 8

c. 10

d. 12

11. Which of the following teams did former Red, Bronson Arroyo NOT play for during his 16-season MLB career?

a. Arizona Diamondbacks

b. St. Louis Cardinals

c. Boston Red Sox

d. Pittsburgh Pirates

12. Bid McPhee played his entire 18-season MLB career with the Cincinnati Reds.

a. True

b. False

13. How many seasons did Johnny Cueto spend with the Cincinnati Reds?

    a. 2

    b. 4

    c. 6

    d. 8

14. How many Silver Slugger Awards did Benito Santiago win during his 20-season MLB career?

    a. 1

    b. 2

    c. 4

    d. 5

15. How many saves did Danny Graves collect for the Cincinnati Reds in 2004?

    a. 40

    b. 41

    c. 44

    d. 45

16. Gary Nolan spent his entire 11-season MLB career with the Cincinnati Reds.

    a. True

    b. False

17. How many seasons did Aroldis Chapman spend with the Cincinnati Reds?

    a. 2

    b. 4

c. 5

d. 6

18. How many World Series championships did Dan Gullet win in his 9-season MLB career?

    a. 0

    b. 1

    c. 2

    d. 3

19. How many seasons did Pete Donohue spend with the Cincinnati Reds?

    a. 12

    b. 10

    c. 5

    d. 3

20. Noodles Hahn played his entire 8-season MLB career with the Cincinnati Reds.

    a. True

    b. False

QUIZ ANSWERS

1. C – Oakland A's

2. A – True

3. D – California Angels

4. B – Philadelphia Phillies

5. B – 3

6. C – 6

7. A – True

8. C – 2

9. D – 6

10. D – 12

11. B – St. Louis Cardinals

12. A – True

13. D – 8

14. C – 4

15. B – 41

16. B – False (He played for the Reds and the California Angels.)

17. D – 6

18. D – 3

19. B – 10

20. B – False (He played for the Reds and the New York Yankees.)

DID YOU KNOW?

1. José Rijo spent 10 seasons of his 14-season MLB career with the Cincinnati Reds. He also played for the Oakland A's and New York Yankees. He is a 1x MLB All-Star, World Series champion, and World Series MVP.

2. Johnny Bench spent his entire 17-season MLB career with the Cincinnati Reds. He is a member of the National Baseball Hall of Fame, 14x MLB All-Star, 10x Gold Glove Award winner, 2x MVP, NL Rookie of the Year, Major League Player of the Year, 2x World Series champion, and World Series MVP.

3. Tom Seaver spent 6 seasons of his 20-season MLB career with the Cincinnati Reds. He also played for the New York Mets, Chicago White Sox, and Boston Red Sox. He is a member of the National Baseball Hall of Fame, 12x MLB All-Star, 3x Cy Young Award winner, NL Rookie of the Year, 3x ERA title winner, and World Series champion.

4. Eppa Rixey spent 13 seasons of his 21-season MLB career with the Cincinnati Reds. He also played for the Philadelphia Phillies. He is a member of the National Baseball Hall of Fame.

5. Bucky Walters spent 11 seasons of his 16-season MLB career with the Cincinnati Reds. He also played for the Philadelphia Phillies and Boston Braves. He was a 6x MLB

All-Star, MVP, Triple Crown winner, 2x ERA title winner, and World Series champion.

6. Jim Maloney spent 11 seasons of his 12-season MLB career with the Cincinnati Reds. He also played for the California Angels. He is a 1x MLB All-Star.

7. Homer Bailey spent 12 seasons of his MLB career with the Cincinnati Reds. He currently plays for the Minnesota Twins. He has also played for the Oakland A's and Kansas City Royals.

8. Bronson Arroyo spent 9 seasons of his 16-season MLB career with the Cincinnati Reds. He also played for the Pittsburgh Pirates, Boston Red Sox, and Arizona Diamondbacks. He is a 1x MLB All-Star, Gold Glove Award winner, and World Series champion.

9. Johnny Cueto spent 8 seasons of his MLB career with the Cincinnati Reds. He currently plays for the San Francisco Giants. He has also played for the Kansas City Royals. As of the end of the 2020 season, he is a 2x MLB All-Star and World Series champion.

10. Aroldis Chapman spent 6 seasons of his MLB career with the Cincinnati Reds. He currently plays for the New York Yankees. He has also played for the Chicago Cubs. As of the end of the 2020 season, he is a 6x MLB All-Star and World Series champion.

CHAPTER 13:

WORLD SERIES

QUIZ TIME!

1. How many World Series championships have the Cincinnati Reds won?

    a. 0

    b. 2

    c. 4

    d. 5

2. How many NL pennants have the Cincinnati Reds won?

    a. 5

    b. 6

    c. 9

    d. 10

3. Which team did the Cincinnati Reds face in the 1919 World Series?

    a. New York Yankees

    b. Chicago White Sox

    c. Boston Red Sox

    d. Detroit Tigers

4. Which team did the Cincinnati Reds face in the 1939 World Series?

   a. New York Yankees
   b. Philadelphia Athletics
   c. Washington Senators
   d. St. Louis Browns

5. Which team did the Cincinnati Reds face in the 1940 World Series?

   a. New York Yankees
   b. Boston Red Sox
   c. Cleveland Indians
   d. Detroit Tigers

6. Which team did the Cincinnati Reds face in the 1961 World Series?

   a. Los Angeles Angels
   b. Baltimore Orioles
   c. New York Yankees
   d. Minnesota Twins

7. The Cincinnati Reds faced the Baltimore Orioles in the 1970 World Series.

   a. True
   b. False

8. Which team did the Cincinnati Reds face in the 1972 World Series?

   a. Kansas City Royals
   b. Detroit Tigers

c. Oakland A's

d. Texas Rangers

9. Which team did the Cincinnati Reds face in the 1975 World Series?

   a. Oakland A's

   b. Boston Red Sox

   c. Milwaukee Brewers

   d. Cleveland Indians

10. Which team did the Cincinnati Reds face in the 1976 World Series?

   a. Baltimore Orioles

   b. Kansas City Royals

   c. California Angels

   d. New York Yankees

11. Which team did the Cincinnati Reds face in the 1990 World Series?

   a. New York Yankees

   b. Oakland A's

   c. Boston Red Sox

   d. Toronto Blue Jays

12. Pat Moran was the manager of the Cincinnati Reds during the 1919 World Series.

   a. True

   b. False

13. Who was manager of the Cincinnati Reds during the 1939 and 1940 World Series'?

a. Fred Hutchinson

b. Jack Hendricks

c. Bill McKechnie

d. Chuck Dressen

14. Who was manager of the Cincinnati Reds during the 1961 World Series?

a. Dick Sisler

b. Fred Hutchinson

c. Dave Bristol

d. Sparky Anderson

15. Who was manager of the Cincinnati Reds during the 1970, 1972, 1975, and 1976 World Series?

a. Lou Piniella

b. Pete Rose

c. John McNamara

d. Sparky Anderson

16. Lou Piniella was the manager of the Cincinnati Reds during the 1990 World Series.

a. True

b. False

17. How many games did the 1939 World Series go?

a. 4

b. 5

c. 6

d. 7

18. How many games did the 1940 World Series go?

    a. 4

    b. 5

    c. 6

    d. 7

19. How many games did the 1961 World Series go?

    a. 4

    b. 5

    c. 6

    d. 7

20. The 1919 World Series went 8 games.

    a. True

    b. False

QUIZ ANSWERS

1. D – 5 (1919, 1940, 1976, 1990)

2. C – 9 (1919, 1939, 1940, 1961, 1970, 1972, 1975, 1976, 1990)

3. B – Chicago White Sox

4. A – New York Yankees

5. D – Detroit Tigers

6. C – New York Yankees

7. A – True

8. C – Oakland A's

9. B – Boston Red Sox

10. D – New York Yankees

11. B – Oakland A's

12. A - True

13. C – Bill McKechnie

14. B – Fred Hutchinson

15. D – Sparky Anderson

16. A – True

17. A – 4

18. D – 7

19. B – 5

20. A – True

DID YOU KNOW?

1. The 1970 World Series went five games, the 1972 World Series went seven games, the 1975 World Series went seven games, the 1976 World Series went four games, and the 1990 World Series went four games.

2. Cincinnati Reds manager Bill McKechnie became the first MLB manager to win a World Series with two different teams.

3. Hod Eller got the Game 8 win in the 1919 World Series; Paul Derringer got the Game 7 win in the 1940 World Series; Clay Carroll got the Game 7 win in the 1975 World Series and Will McEnaney got the save; Gary Nolan got the Game 4 win in the 1976 World Series and McEnaney also got that save, José Rijo got the win in Game 4 of the 1990 World Series and Randy Myers got the save.

4. The 1976 Reds to this day are the only team in MLB history to sweep an entire tiered postseason. The Reds are the most recent National League team to win back-to-back World Series'. The 1976 World Series was the second time that the New York Yankees were swept in a World Series.

5. The 1975 World Series is the earliest World Series that survives today on video in its entirety.

6. The 1961 World Series was full of Cold War political puns including the "Reds" against the "Yanks."

7. Here are the durations of every World Series the Reds played in: 1919 World Series, October 1-9; 1939 World Series, October 4-8; 1940 World Series, October 2-8; 1961 World Series, October 4-9; 1970 World Series, October 10-15; 1972 World Series, October 14- 22; 1975 World Series, October 11-22; 1976 World Series, October 16- 21; 1990 World Series, October 16- 20.

8. Game 2 of the 1976 World Series at Riverfront Stadium was the first World Series weekend game to be played at night.

9. 1976 was the final World Series broadcast out of 30 consecutive World Series telecasts by NBC.

10. As of 2020, the 1990 World Series remains the most recent appearance in the World Series for both the Reds and the Oakland A's.

CHAPTER 14:

HEATED RIVALRIES

QUIZ TIME!

1. Which team does NOT play in the National League Central with the Cincinnati Reds?

    a. Pittsburgh Pirates

    b. St. Louis Cardinals

    c. Chicago Cubs

    d. Cleveland Indians

2. The Cincinnati Reds were in the National League West Division from 1969 to 1993.

    a. True

    b. False

3. Which team below was once a member of the NL Central Division?

    a. Kansas City Royals

    b. Houston Astros

    c. Detroit Tigers

    d. Minnesota Twins

4. What current National League Central team has won the most NL Central championships?

    a. Chicago Cubs
    b. Milwaukee Brewers
    c. St. Louis Cardinals
    d. Cincinnati Reds

5. What is a series between the Reds and Ohio rival Cleveland Indians called?

    a. Ohio Series
    b. Battle of Ohio
    c. I-71 Series
    d. Battle of I-71

6. What year did the Reds and Indians meet for the first time?

    a. 1990
    b. 1993
    c. 1997
    d. 1998

7. The winner of the Battle of Ohio gets possession of the "Ohio Cup."

    a. True
    b. False

8. The Reds have won five World Series championships. How many have the Chicago Cubs won?

    a. 1
    b. 2

c. 3

d. 4

9. The Reds have won five World Series championships. How many have the Cleveland Indians won?

   a. 0

   b. 1

   c. 2

   d. 3

10. The Reds have won five World Series championships. How many have the Milwaukee Brewers won?

   a. 0

   b. 1

   c. 2

   d. 3

11. The Reds have won five World Series championships. How many have the Pittsburgh Pirates won?

   a. 0

   b. 2

   c. 4

   d. 5

12. The St. Louis Cardinals have won 11 World Series championships.

   a. True

   b. False

13. Which player has NOT played for both the Reds and the Chicago Cubs?

a. Aroldis Chapman

b. Joe Morgan

c. Lonny Frey

d. David Ross

14. Which player has NOT played for both the Reds and the Cleveland Indians?

    a. Jay Bruce

    b. Vada Pinson

    c. José Rijo

    d. Frank Robinson

15. Which player has NOT played for both the Reds and the Milwaukee Brewers?

    a. Mike Moustakas

    b. Dave Parker

    c. Kyle Lohse

    d. George Foster

16. In 1994, when the NL Central Division was created, the Pittsburgh Pirates were originally supposed to stay in the East while the Atlanta Braves were supposed to move to the Central from the West.

    a. True

    b. False

17. Which player has NOT played for both the Reds and the Pittsburgh Pirates?

    a. Bronson Arroyo

    b. Scott Rolen

    c. Heinie Groh

    d. Ted Kluszewski

18. Which player has NOT played for both the Reds and the St. Louis Cardinals?

    a. Eric Davis

    b. Dan Driessen

    c. Reggie Sanders

    d. Bill Doran

19. How many AL Central Division titles did the Houston Astros win before they moved to the AL West?

    a. 0

    b. 1

    c. 3

    d. 4

20. The Pittsburgh Pirates have won the fewest NL Central Division titles at 0.

    a. True

    b. False

QUIZ ANSWERS

1. D – Cleveland Indians

2. A – True

3. B – Houston Astros

4. C – St. Louis Cardinals (11)

5. B – Battle of Ohio

6. C – 1997

7. A – True

8. C – 3

9. C – 2

10. A – 0

11. D – 5

12. A – True

13. B – Joe Morgan

14. C – José Rijo

15. D – George Foster

16. A- True

17. B – Scott Rolen

18. D – Bill Doran

19. D – 4

20. A – True

DID YOU KNOW?

1. The St. Louis Cardinals have won the most National League Central Division championships with 11 (as of the end of the 2020 season). The Chicago Cubs won 6, the Cincinnati Reds won 3, the Milwaukee Brewers won 2, and the Pittsburgh Pirates haven't won any. The Houston Astros, formerly of the NL Central, won 4 division titles during their time in the NL Central. The most recent NL Central Division champions are the Chicago Cubs (2020). The Reds have not won the NL Central since 2012 (as of the end of the 2020 season). The Reds won the division in 1995, 2010, and 2012 and they won the NL West 7 times, in 1970, 1972, 1973, 1975, 1976, 1979, and 1990.

2. A series between the Cincinnati Reds and Cleveland Indians is often referred to as the "Battle of Ohio." The winner possesses the "Ohio Cup." The Reds and Indians are 249 miles apart via I-71. Progressive Field is further northeast than Great American Ball Park.

3. In 1998, the NL Central became the largest division in the MLB when the Milwaukee Brewers were moved in from the American League Central. It was the largest until the Houston Astros moved to the AL West in 2013.

4. The National League Central has been dominated by the St. Louis Cardinals. The Cards have accounted for 11 of the 25 division championships plus three wild card berths.

5. The Pittsburgh Pirates have not won the NL Central Division since it was created but they have won three wild card berths.

6. Mordecai Brown, Jonathan Broxton, César Cedeño, Dave Collins, Eric Davis, Paul Derringer, Dan Driessen, Frank Dwyer, Jim Edmonds, Curt Flood, Ron Gant, Clint Hurdle, Jason LaRue, Ryan Ludwick, Tony Mullane, Vada Pinson, Cookie Rojas, Scott Rolen, Chris Sabo, Reggie Sanders, and Bobby Tolan have all played for both the Cincinnati Reds and the St. Louis Cardinals.

7. Yonder Alonso, Trevor Bauer, Buddy Bell, Aaron Boone, Jay Bruce, Marlon Byrd, Orlando Cabrera, Leo Cárdenas, Sean Casey, Bruce Chen, Shin-Soo Choo, Gordy Coleman, Pete Donohue, Edwin Encarnación, Hank Foiles, Terry Francona, Danny Graves, Tommy Harper, Austin Kearns, Bob Kelly, Marty Keough, Johnny Klippstein, Larry Kopf, Cliff Lee, Ryan Ludwick, Billy Martin, Kent Mercker, Kevin Mitchell, Don Newcombe, Brandon Phillips, Vada Pinson, Wally Post, Yasiel Puig, Bip Roberts, Frank Robinson, Drew Stubbs, and David Weathers have all played for both the Cincinnati Reds and the Cleveland Indians.

8. Mordecai Brown, Marlon Byrd, Aroldis Chapman, Ryan Dempster, Chris Denorfia, Paul Derringer, Frank Dwyer, Jim Edmonds, Scott Feldman, Terry Francona, Lonny Frey, Ival Goodman, Willie Greene, Billy Hamilton, Bubbles Hargrave, Lenny Harris, Grady Hatton, César Izturis, Marty Keough, Johnny Klippstein, Dave Martinez, Lloyd

McClendon, Kent Mercker, Dioner Navarro, Ramon Ortiz, David Ross, Benito Santiago, Todd Walker, and Don Zimmer have all played for both the Cincinnati Reds and the Chicago Cubs.

9. Jonathan Broxton, Francisco Cordero, Bill Doran, Jim Edmonds, Terry Francona, César Izturis, Kyle Lohse, Wade Miley, Mike Moustakas, Joe Oliver, Dave Parker, and David Weathers have all played for both the Cincinnati Reds and the Milwaukee Brewers.

10. Bronson Arroyo, Bo Belinsky, Gus Bell, Smoky Burgess, Marlon Byrd, Sean Casey, Pop Corkhill, Spud Davis, Zach Duke, Pat Duncan, Hank Foiles, Heinie Groh, José Guillen, Harry Gumbert, Tommy Helms, Rollie Hemsley, Bill Henry, Babe Herman, César Izturis, Ted Kluszewski, Cliff Lee, Red Lucas, Ryan Ludwick, Paul Moskau, Dave Parker, Ted Power, Joe Randa, Pokey Reese, David Ross, Reggie Sanders, Benito Santiago, and Bobby Tolan have all played for both the Cincinnati Reds and the Pittsburgh Pirates.

CHAPTER 15:

THE AWARDS SECTION

QUIZ TIME!

1. Which Cincinnati Reds player won the National League MVP Award in 1975 AND 1976?

    a. George Foster

    b. Johnny Bench

    c. Joe Morgan

    d. Pete Rose

2. As of the end of the 2020 season, Jack McKeon is the only Cincinnati Reds manager ever to win the National League Manager of the Year Award.

    a. True

    b. False

3. Who is the only Cincinnati Reds player ever to win a National League Cy Young Award?

    a. Bronson Arroyo

    b. Trevor Bauer

    c. Aroldis Chapman

    d. Johnny Cueto

4. Which Cincinnati Reds player most recently won the National League Rookie of the Year Award?

    a. Pete Rose

    b. Chris Sabo

    c. Joey Votto

    d. Scott Williamson

5. Who is the only pitcher in Cincinnati Reds history to win a pitching Triple Crown?

    a. Noodles Hahn

    b. Trevor Bauer

    c. Bucky Walters

    d. Johnny Cueto

6. Which Cincinnati Reds player won a Silver Slugger Award in 2011?

    a. Jay Bruce

    b. Brandon Phillips

    c. Joey Votto

    d. Todd Frazier

7. No Cincinnati Reds player has ever won the MLB Home Run Derby.

    a. True

    b. False

8. Which Cincinnati Reds player was named the DHL Hometown Hero (Voted by MLB fans as the most outstanding player in franchise history)?

    a. Pete Rose

    b. Johnny Bench

   c. Barry Larkin

   d. Frank Robinson

9. Who was the first Cincinnati Reds player to win a National League Gold Glove Award?

   a. Leo Cárdenas

   b. Frank Robinson

   c. Harvey Haddix

   d. Roy McMillan

10. Who was the first Cincinnati Reds player to win a Silver Slugger Award?

   a. Dave Concepción

   b. George Foster

   c. Joe Morgan

   d. Both A and B

11. Which Cincinnati Reds pitcher won the National League Rolaids Relief Man of the Year Award in 1996?

   a. Jeff Shaw

   b. Johnny Ruffin

   c. Jeff Brantley

   d. Hector Carrasco

12. Johnny Bench was named the National League MVP in 1970 and 1972.

   a. True

   b. False

13. What year was Frank Robinson named the National League Rookie of the Year?

a. 1955

b. 1956

c. 1957

d. 1958

14. Who was named the MLB All-Star Game MVP in 1980?

    a. George Foster

    b. Dave Concepción

    c. Johnny Bench

    d. Ken Griffey Sr.

15. In 2011, Cincinnati Reds players Brandon Phillips and which other player won National League Gold Glove Awards?

    a. Scott Rolen

    b. Joey Votto

    c. Jay Bruce

    d. Todd Frazier

16. Johnny Cueto won the 2014 MLB Wilson Defensive Player of the Year Award.

    a. True

    b. False

17. Which Cincinnati Reds player was named the 1967 MLB All-Star Game MVP?

    a. Johnny Bench

    b. Vada Pinson

    c. Pete Rose

    d. Tony Pérez

18. Which Cincinnati Reds player won a Silver Slugger Award in 1995?

    a. Bret Boone
    b. Barry Larkin
    c. Reggie Sanders
    d. Hal Morris

19. Which Cincinnati Reds player was named the 1938 National League MVP?

    a. Bucky Walters
    b. Frank McCormick
    c. Ernie Lombardi
    d. Lonny Frey

20. Johnny Bench NEVER won a Silver Slugger Award.

    a. True
    b. False

QUIZ ANSWERS

1. C – Joe Morgan

2. A – True (1999)

3. B – Trevor Bauer (2020)

4. D – Scott Williamson (1999)

5. C – Bucky Walters (1939)

6. B – Brandon Phillips

7. B – False, Dave Parker (1985), Eric Davis (1989), Todd Frazier (2015)

8. A – Pete Rose

9. D – Roy McMillan (1957)

10. D – Both A and B (1981)

11. C – Jeff Brantley

12. A- True

13. B – 1956

14. D – Ken Griffey Sr.

15. B – Joey Votto

16. A – True

17. D – Tony Pérez

18. B – Barry Larkin

19. C – Ernie Lombardi

20. A – True

DID YOU KNOW?

1. The Cincinnati Reds have only had ONE Cy Young Award winner in franchise history, and it was VERY recent: Trevor Bauer in 2020.

2. Nine different Reds players have won Silver Slugger Awards: Joe Morgan, Brandon Phillips, Dave Concepción (2), Barry Larkin (9), Felipe López, George Foster, Dave Parker (2), Eric Davis (2), and Jay Bruce (2).

3. Seven different Reds have been named National League Rookie of the Year: Frank Robinson (1956), Pete Rose (1963), Tommy Helms (1966), Johnny Bench (1968), Pat Zachry (1976), Chris Sabo (1988), and Scott Williamson (1999).

4. The Cincinnati Reds have had 21 different players win National League Gold Glove Awards: Harvey Haddix, Bronson Arroyo, Johnny Edwards (2), Johnny Bench (10), Tucker Barnhart (2), Joey Votto, Tommy Helms (2), Joe Morgan (5), Bret Boone, Pokey Reese (2), Brandon Phillips (4), Scott Rolen, Roy McMillan (3), Leo Cárdenas, Dave Concepción (5), Barry Larkin (3), Frank Robinson, Vada Pinson, Pete Rose (2), César Gerónimo and Eric Davis (3).

5. The Cincinnati Reds have had 12 different players win the National League MVP Award: Ernie Lombardi (1938), Bucky Walters (1939), Frank McCormick (1940), Frank Robinson (1961), Johnny Bench (1970 and 1972), Pete Rose

(1973), Joe Morgan (1975 and 1976), George Foster (1977), Barry Larkin (1995), and Joey Votto (2010).

6. Four different Cincinnati Reds players have won the National League Rolaids Relief Man of the Year Award: Rawly Eastwick (1976), John Franco (1988), Jeff Brantley (1996), and Jeff Shaw (1997).

7. The Cincinnati Reds have had five different players win the MLB All-Star Game MVP Award: Tony Pérez (1967), Joe Morgan (1972), George Foster (1976), Ken Griffey Sr. (1980), and Dave Concepción (1982).

8. The Cincinnati Reds as a team won the 2012 Baseball America Organization of the Year Award and the 2014 Wilson Defensive Team of the Year Award.

9. Joey Votto won the 2010 National League Hank Aaron Award. This award is given annually to a player who is selected as the best hitter in the league as voted by fans and media.

10. Brandon Phillips won the 2012 Wilson Defensive Player of the Year Award and Jay Bruce won the award in 2013.

CHAPTER 16:

CINCY

QUIZ TIME!

1. Which famous Hollywood director was born in Cincinnati?

    a. Quentin Tarantino
    b. James Cameron
    c. Steven Spielberg
    d. Martin Scorsese

2. Cincinnatians eat over two million pounds of chili each year.

    a. True
    b. False

3. Which former U.S. President was born in Cincinnati?

    a. Barack Obama
    b. William Howard Taft
    c. John F. Kennedy
    d. Teddy Roosevelt

4. Which famous NASA astronaut taught aeronautical engineering at the University of Cincinnati from 1971 to 1979?

   a. John Glenn
   b. Sally Ride
   c. Buzz Aldrin
   d. Neil Armstrong

5. Which popular children's toy was invented in Cincinnati?

   a. Beanie Baby
   b. Furby
   c. Magic 8 Ball
   d. Barbie Doll

6. What percentage of the U.S. population lives within half a day's drive from Cincinnati?

   a. 20
   b. 40
   c. 60
   d. 80

7. Cincinnati is the capital of the game "cornhole."

   a. True
   b. False

8. What is the name of Cincinnati's NFL team?

   a. Cincinnati 49ers
   b. Cincinnati Bengals
   c. Cincinnati Cowboys
   d. Cincinnati Buccaneers

9. What is the name of Cincinnati's MLS team?

    a. Sporting Cincinnati
    b. Cincinnati Galaxy
    c. Cincinnati Union
    d. FC Cincinnati

10. Which Cincinnati franchise were a professional basketball team in the NBA from 1957 to 1972 and are now known as the Sacramento Kings?

    a. Warriors
    b. Kings
    c. Royals
    d. Cardinals

11. What is the name of the Bengals' current stadium?

    a. Levi's Stadium
    b. Paul Brown Stadium
    c. Arrowhead Stadium
    d. State Farm Stadium

12. Slaves used Cincinnati as a stop on the Underground Railroad on their way to Canada.

    a. True
    b. False

13. What is the name of FC Cincinnati's stadium, which will open in May 2021?

    a. Audi Field
    b. Children's Mercy Park
    c. West End Stadium
    d. Red Bull Field

14. The city of Cincinnati has a subway system that was built, never used, and left abandoned.

    a. True
    b. False

15. How many Super Bowl championships have the Cincinnati Bengals?

    a. 0
    b. 1
    c. 2
    d. 3

16. Cult leader Charles Manson was born in Cincinnati.

    a. True
    b. False

17. How many times has FC Cincinnati won the MLS?

    a. 0
    b. 1
    c. 2
    d. 3

18. What is Cincinnati/Northern Kentucky International Airport's code?

    a. NKC
    b. CKI
    c. CNK
    d. CVG

19. Cincinnati was the first city in the United States to establish which first professional and fully paid front line profession?

  a. Hospital staff
  b. Police department
  c. Fire department
  d. News organization staff

20. The inventor of the Pringles can is buried in Cincinnati...in a Pringles can.

  a. True
  b. False

QUIZ ANSWERS

1. C – Steven Spielberg

2. A - True

3. B – William Howard Taft

4. D – Neil Armstrong

5. C – Magic 8 Ball

6. C – 60

7. A- True

8. B – Cincinnati Bengals

9. D – FC Cincinnati

10. C – Royals

11. B – Paul Brown Stadium

12. A- True

13. C – West End Stadium

14. A – True

15. A – 0

16. A – True

17. A – 0

18. D – CVG

19. C – Fire department

20. A – True

DID YOU KNOW?

1. A wreath that was on Abraham Lincoln's casket after his assassination is displayed at Memorial Hall in Cincy.

2. The last known passenger pigeon, named Martha, died at the Cincinnati Zoo in 1914.

3. Cincinnati was home to the first newspaper printed in the Northwest, *The Centinel of the Northwest Territory.*

4. The Cincinnati Library has cameras, 3D printers, audio-visual equipment, sewing machines, laser cutters, engravers, and other tools that members can use for free…. They do have books too.

5. The first recorded crime in Cincinnati was cucumber theft.

6. The Cincinnati Cyclones hockey team is a minor league affiliate of the Buffalo Sabres of the NHL.

7. Goetta is a German sausage mash that is popular in Cincinnati. It is mainly composed of ground meat, oats, and spices.

8. The Cincinnati Zoo is the fourth oldest zoo in the United States.

9. The Procter & Gamble Company was founded in Cincinnati in 1837 as a candle and soapmaking business by William Procter and James Gamble.

10. Cincinnati is surrounded by seven hills: Mount Adams, Mount Auburn, Walnut Hills, Fairmount, Fairview Heights, Clifton Heights, and Mt. Harrison.

CHAPTER 17:

LITTLE GENERAL

QUIZ TIME!

1. What is Johnny Bench's full name?

    a. Johnny James Bench

    b. Eugene Johnny Bench

    c. Jonathan Lee Bench

    d. Johnny Lee Bench

2. Johnny Bench played his entire 17-season MLB career with the Cincinnati Reds.

    a. True

    b. False

3. Where was Johnny Bench born?

    a. Tulsa, Oklahoma

    b. Binger, Oklahoma

    c. Oklahoma City, Oklahoma

    d. Checotah, Oklahoma

4. When was Johnny Bench born?

a. March 7, 1947

b. March 7, 1957

c. December 7, 1947

d. December 7, 1957

5. Johnny Bench was named the 1968 National League Rookie of the Year.

   a. True

   b. False

6. How many Gold Glove Awards did Johnny Bench win in his 17-season MLB career?

   a. 8

   b. 9

   c. 10

   d. 11

7. What year was Johnny Bench inducted into the National Baseball Hall of Fame?

   a. 1988

   b. 1989

   c. 1991

   d. 1993

8. Johnny Bench was named the National League MVP in 1970 and 1972.

   a. True

   b. False

9. How many World Series championships did Johnny Bench win during his 17-season MLB career?

a. 0

b. 1

c. 2

d. 3

10. What year did Johnny Bench make his MLB debut?

    a. 1970

    b. 1969

    c. 1968

    d. 1967

11. How many MLB All-Star Games was Johnny Bench named to in his 17-season MLB career?

    a. 12

    b. 13

    c. 14

    d. 15

12. The Cincinnati Reds retired Johnny Bench's No. 5 on August 11, 1984.

    a. True

    b. False

13. Johnny Bench led the National League in home runs in 1970 and which year?

    a. 1971

    b. 1972

    c. 1973

    d. 1975

14. On September 17, 2011, the Cincinnati Reds unveiled a statue of Johnny Bench at the Reds Hall of Fame entrance at Great American Ball Park.

    a. True
    b. False

15. Johnny Bench led the National League in RBIs in 1970, 1972 and which year?

    a. 1968
    b. 1969
    c. 1973
    d. 1974

16. What year was Johnny Bench inducted into the Cincinnati Reds Hall of Fame?

    a. 1985
    b. 1986
    c. 1988
    d. 1989

17. From 2000 through 2018, the best collegiate catcher received the annual Johnny Bench Award.

    a. True
    b. False

18. How many home runs did Johnny Bench hit in his 17-season MLB career?

    a. 189
    b. 289
    c. 389
    d. 489

19. How many RBI did Johnny Bench collect in his MLB career?

    a. 976

    b. 1,176

    c. 1,276

    d. 1,376

20. Johnny Bench was named the 1976 World Series MVP.

    a. True

    b. False

QUIZ ANSWERS

1. D – Johnny Lee Bench

2. A – True

3. C – Oklahoma City, Oklahoma

4. C – December 7, 1947

5. A – True

6. C – 10

7. B – 1989

8. A – True

9. C – 2

10. D – 1967

11. C – 14

12. A – True

13. B – 1972

14. A – True

15. D – 1974

16. B – 1986

17. A – True

18. C – 389

19. D – 1,376

20. A – True

DID YOU KNOW?

1. Johnny Bench was named to the MLB All-Century Team and the All-Time Team.

2. In 2003, Johnny Bench guest-starred on an episode of *Yes, Dear* as himself, alongside Ernie Banks and Frank Robinson.

3. In 2008, Johnny Bench co-wrote the book *Catch Every Ball: How to Handle Life's Pitches*. In 1979, Bench co-wrote an autobiography entitled *Catch You Later*.

4. In 1999, Johnny Bench ranked at Number 16 on Sporting News' list of the 100 Greatest Baseball Players. He was the highest-ranking catcher to make the list.

5. Johnny Bench hosted the TVseries *The Baseball Bunch* from 1982 to 1985.

6. Johnny Bench was elected to the National Baseball Hall of Fame in 1989 alongside Carl Yastrzemski.

7. In 1989, Johnny Bench became the first individual baseball player to appear on a box of Wheaties.

8. During the 1980s, Johnny Bench was a spokesman in commercials for Krylon paint. His catchphrase was: "I'm Johnny Bench, and this is Johnny Bench's bench."

9. After turning 50, Johnny Bench became a part-time professional golfer and played in several events on the Senior PGA Tour.

10. Johnny Bench has been married four times.

CHAPTER 18:

LARK

QUIZ TIME!

1. Where was Barry Larkin born?

   a. Ann Arbor, Michigan
   b. Chicago, Illinois
   c. Cincinnati, Ohio
   d. Cleveland, Ohio

2. Barry Larkin played for the 1984 U.S. Olympics men's baseball team.

   a. True
   b. False

3. How many Silver Slugger Awards did Barry Larkin win during his 19-season MLB career?

   a. 7
   b. 8
   c. 9
   d. 10

4. How many Gold Glove Awards did Barry Larkin win?

  a. 0

  b. 1

  c. 2

  d. 3

5. How many MLB All-Star Games was Barry Larkin named to?

  a. 15

  b. 12

  c. 10

  d. 8

6. What year was Barry Larkin inducted into the National Baseball Hall of Fame?

  a. 2010

  b. 2012

  c. 2014

  d. 2016

7. Barry Larkin accepted a scholarship to play football at the University of Michigan but during his freshman year, he decided to play baseball exclusively.

  a. True

  b. False

8. What year did the Cincinnati Reds retire Barry Larkin's No. 11?

  a. 2007

  b. 2008

c. 2010

d. 2012

9. What year was Barry Larkin inducted into the Cincinnati Reds Hall of Fame?

    a. 2005

    b. 2007

    c. 2008

    d. 2009

10. How many games did Barry Larkin play in the minor leagues?

    a. 77

    b. 177

    c. 277

    d. 377

11. What was Barry Larkin's career batting average?

    a. .275

    b. .285

    c. .295

    d. .305

12. Barry Larkin's daughter, Brielle D'Shea, is named after Shea Stadium.

    a. True

    b. False

13. How many home runs did Barry Larkin hit in his 19-season MLB career?

a. 188

b. 198

c. 208

d. 218

14. How many RBI did Barry Larkin collect?

a. 900

b. 930

c. 960

d. 1000

15. How many bases did Barry Larkin steal in his MLB career?

a. 349

b. 359

c. 369

d. 379

16. On June 27–28, 1991, Barry Larkin became the first shortstop ever to hit five home runs in the span of two consecutive games.

a. True

b. False

17. Barry Larkin was named the National League MVP in what year?

a. 1993

b. 1995

c. 1998

d. 1999

18. How many World Series championships did Barry Larkin win?

    a. 0
    b. 1
    c. 2
    d. 3

19. What other MLB team did Barry Larkin play for?

    a. Oakland A's
    b. New York Mets
    c. Los Angeles Dodgers
    d. He played his entire career with the Cincinnati Reds

20. In 2012, Cincinnati deli, Izzy's created the "Barry Larkin Triple Play" sandwich in honor of Larkin.

    a. True
    b. False

QUIZ ANSWERS

1. C – Cincinnati, Ohio

2. A – True

3. C – 9

4. D – 3

5. B – 12

6. B – 2012

7. A – True

8. D – 2012

9. C – 2008

10. B – 177

11. C - .295

12. A – True

13. B – 198

14. C – 960

15. D – 379

16. A – True

17. B – 1995

18. B – 1 (1990)

19. D – He played his entire career with the Cincinnati Reds

20. A – True

DID YOU KNOW?

1. After he retired from playing, Barry Larkin was hired as a special assistant to the general manager in the Washington Nationals organization.

2. In 2008, Barry Larkin became a studio analyst on MLB Network. In 2011, he became an analyst on ESPN's *Baseball Tonight*.

3. Larkin was the bench coach for the United States in the 2009 World Baseball Classic and managed the United States' second-round game against Puerto Rico when manager Davey Johnson left to attend a wedding. Larkin managed Brazil's national team in the 2013 World Baseball Classic.

4. Barry Larkin made his MLB debut on August 13, 1986, against the San Francisco Giants. Larkin played his final game in the MLB on October 3, 2004, against the Pittsburgh Pirates.

5. The Cincinnati Reds drafted Barry Larkin twice, once out of high school and again out of college. They really wanted their hometown hero.

6. Barry Larkin was named the Reds' captain before the 1997 season, making him the first player to be named captain since Dave Concepción's retirement.

7. On September 27, 1998, Barry Larkin, his brother Stephen Larkin, second baseman Bret Boone, and third baseman Aaron Boone all played the infield at the same time for the last game of the 1998 season, making it the first time in MLB history that two sets of siblings were on the field at the same time.

8. Barry Larkin won a Roberto Clemente Award in 1993. This award is given annually to a player who "best exemplifies the game of baseball, sportsmanship, community involvement, and the individual's contribution to his team," as voted by baseball fans and members of the media.

9. Barry Larkin was named the Big Ten Player of the Year in 1984. His No. 16 was retired by the University of Michigan in 2010.

10. Barry Larkin's son Shane played in the NBA from 2014 to 2018. He played for the Dallas Mavericks, New York Knicks, Brooklyn Nets, and Boston Celtics.

CONCLUSION

Learn anything new? Now you truly are the ultimate Reds fan! Not only did you learn about the Reds of the modern era, but you also expanded your knowledge back to the Big Red Machine and the early days of the franchise.

You learned about the Reds' origins and their history and where they came from. You learned about the history of their uniforms and jersey numbers, you identified some famous quotes and read some of the craziest nicknames of all time.

You learned more about the legendary Johnny Bench, the Hall-of-Famer Barry Larkin, and hustlin' Pete Rose. You were amazed by Reds stats and recalled some of the most famous Reds trades and drafts/draft picks of all time. Your new knowledge was broken down by outfielders, infielders, pitchers, and catchers. You looked back on the Reds' championships and playoff feats and the awards that came before, after, and during them. You also learned about the Reds' fiercest rivalries both within their division and outside it.

Every team in the MLB has a storied history but the Reds have one of the most memorable of all. They have won five World

Series championships with the backing of their devoted fans. Being the ultimate Reds fan takes knowledge and a whole lot of patience, which you tested with this book. Whether you knew every answer or were stumped by several questions, you learned some of the most interesting history that the game of baseball has to offer.

The deep history of the Cincinnati Reds franchise represents what we all love about the game of baseball. The heart, the determination, the tough times, and the unexpected moments, plus the players that inspire us and encourage us to do our best because even if you get knocked down, there is always another game and another day.

With players like Joey Votto, Mike Moustakas, and Eugenio Suarez, the future continues to look bright for the Reds. They have a lot to prove but there is no doubt that this franchise will continue to be one of the most competitive teams in Major League Baseball year after year.

It's a new decade, which means there is a clean slate, ready to continue writing the history of the Cincinnati Reds. The ultimate Reds fan cannot wait to see what's to come for their beloved boys from Cincy.

Made in United States
Cleveland, OH
04 March 2025

14902015R00085